GUITAR

CW00376881

**Wise Publications**
part of The Music Sales Group
London / New York / Paris / Sydney / Copenhagen / Berlin / Madrid / Tokyo

Published by:
Wise Publications,
8/9 Frith Street, London, W1D 3JB, England.

Exclusive distributors:
Music Sales Limited,
Distribution Centre, Newmarket Road,
Bury St Edmunds, Suffolk, IP33 3YB, England.

Music Sales Pty Limited,
120 Rothschild Avenue, Rosebery,
NSW 2018, Australia.

Order No. AM981332
ISBN 1-84449-800-X
This book © Copyright 2004 by Wise Publications.

Music arranged by Matt Cowe.
Music processed by Paul Ewers Music Design.

Printed in the United Kingdom.

www.musicsales.com

Leave Me Alone 12

Rock n Roll Lies  5

Vice 18

Up All Night 25

Which Way Is Out 32

Rip It Up 37

Don't Go Back To Dalston 42

Golden Touch 46

Stumble And Fall 53

Get It And Go 80

In The City 60

To The Sea 68

Fall, Fall, Fall 76


Guitar Tablature Explained 87

# Leave Me Alone

Song By Johnny Borrell
Music By Razorlight

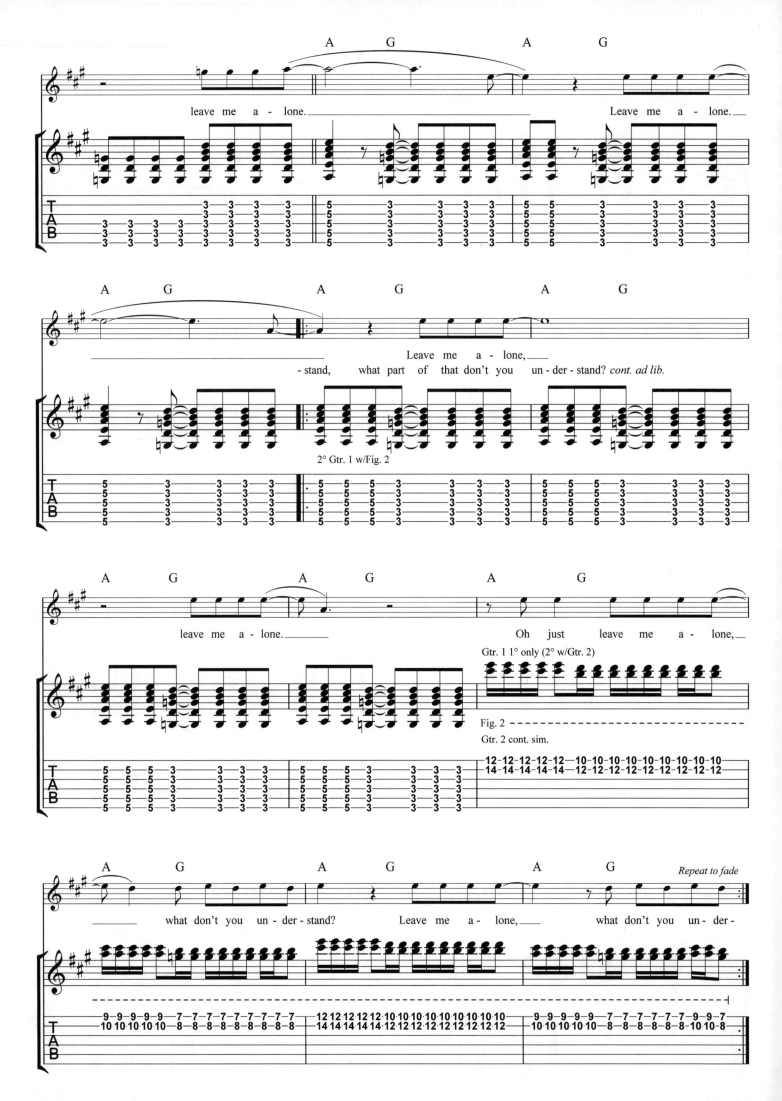

10

# Rock n Roll Lies

### Song By Johnny Borrell and John Fortis
### Music By Razorlight

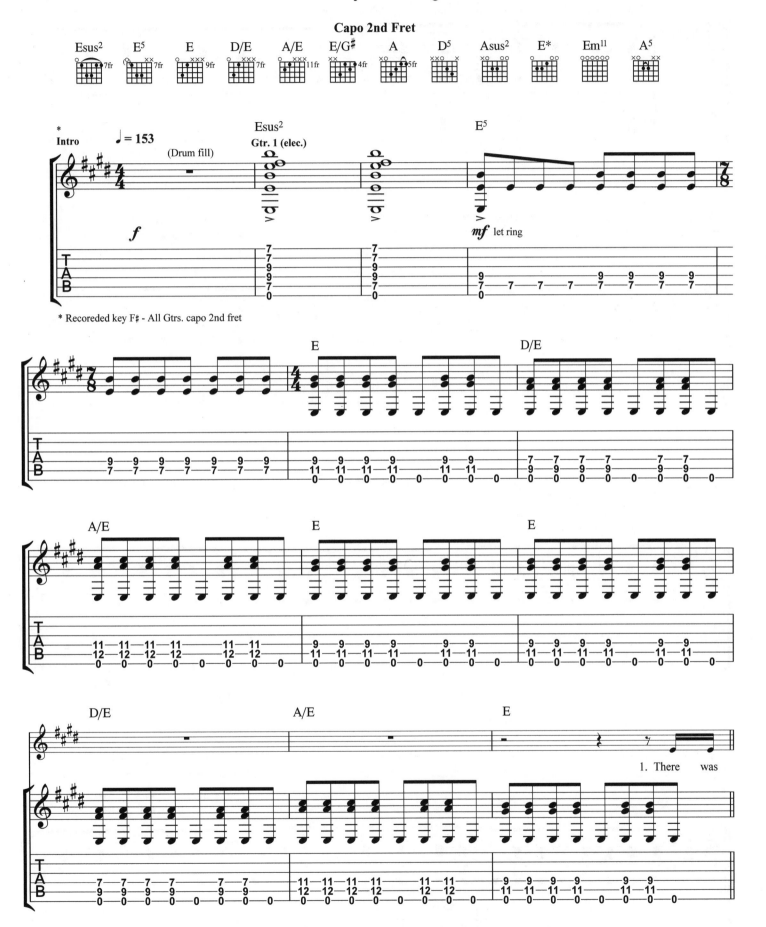

\* Recoreded key F# - All Gtrs. capo 2nd fret

1. There was

12

16

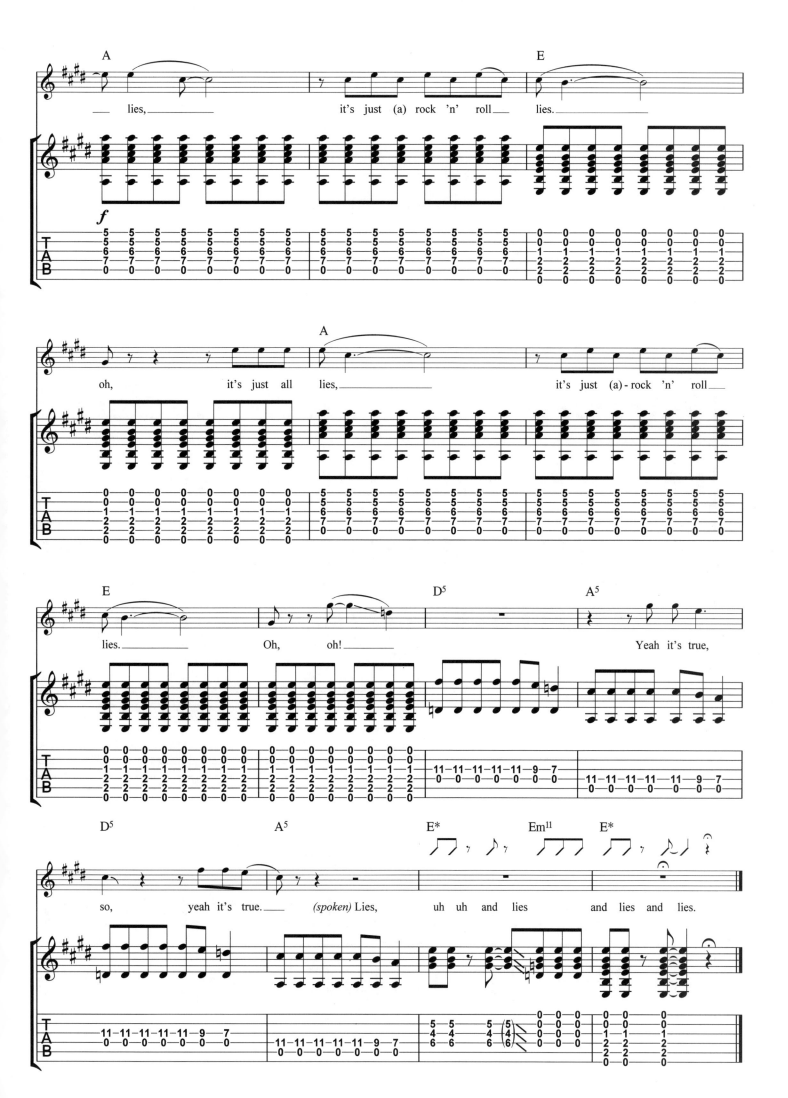

# Vice

### Song By Johnny Borrell
### Music By Razorlight

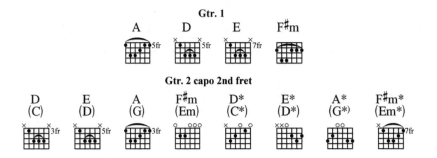

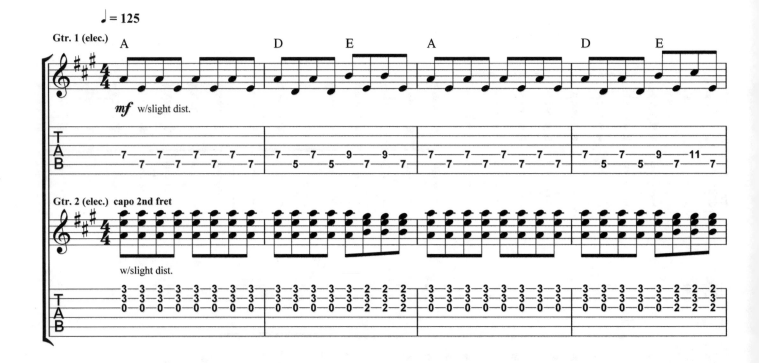

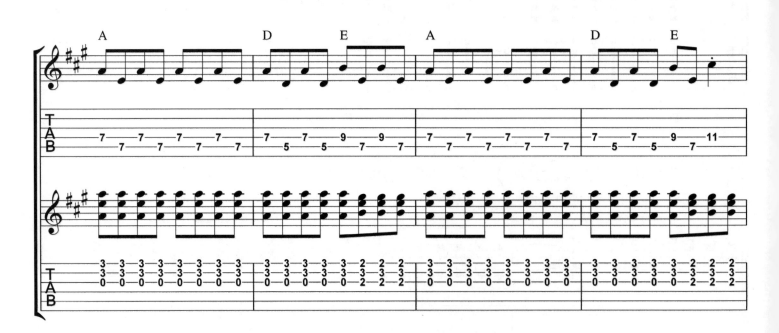

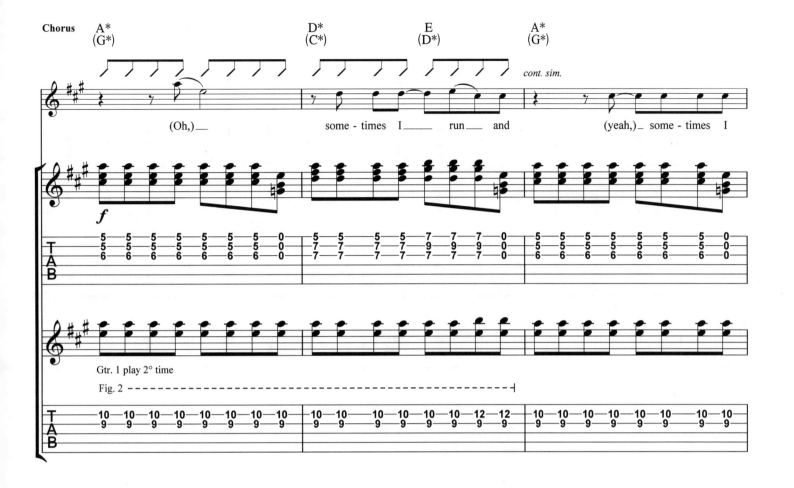

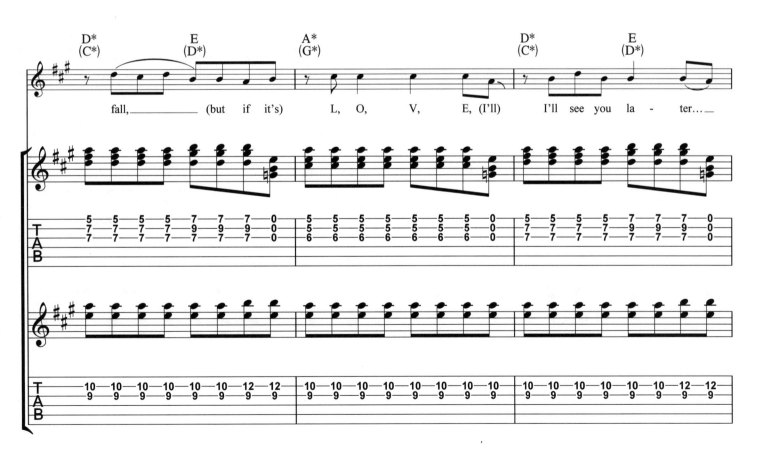

# Up All Night

**Song By Johnny Borrell**
**Music By Razorlight**

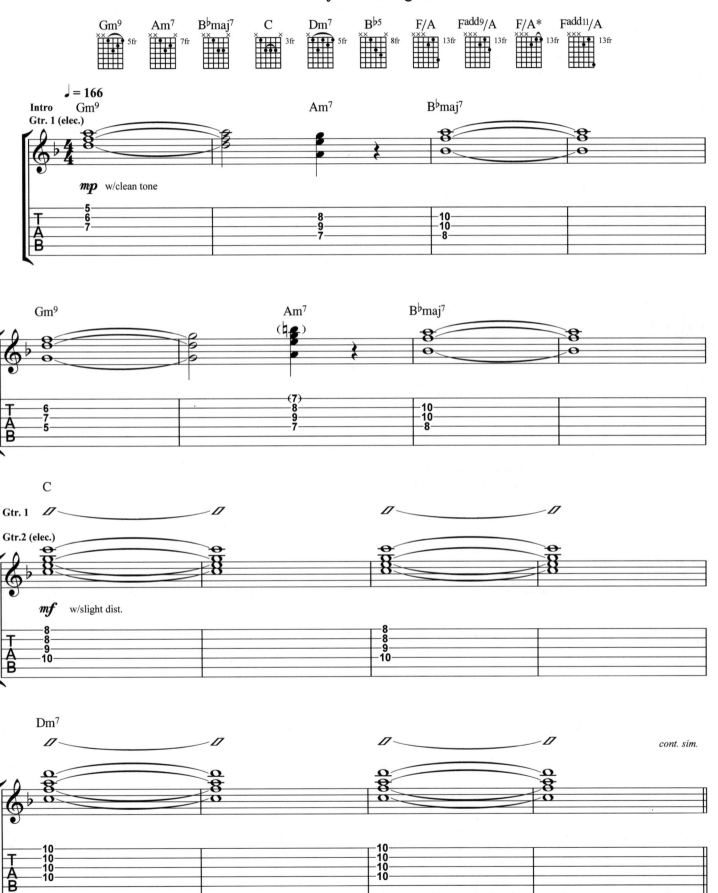

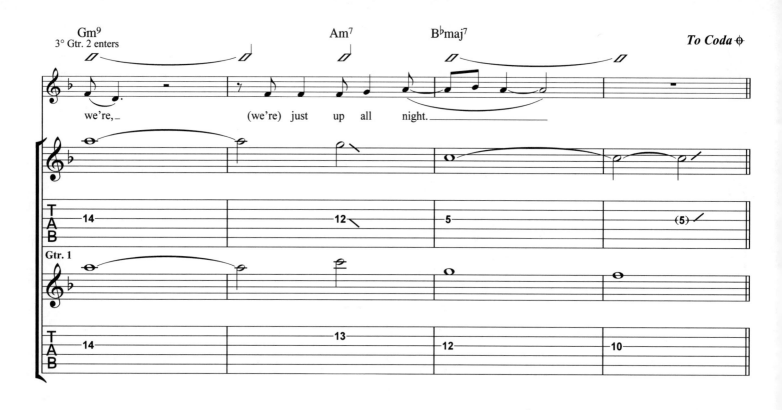

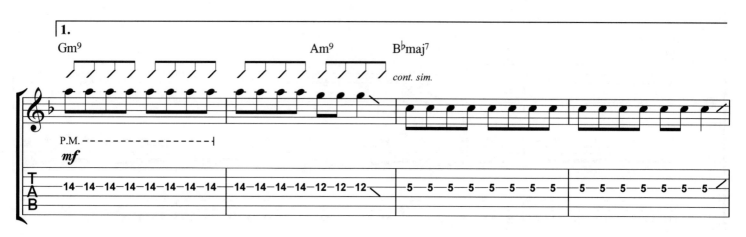

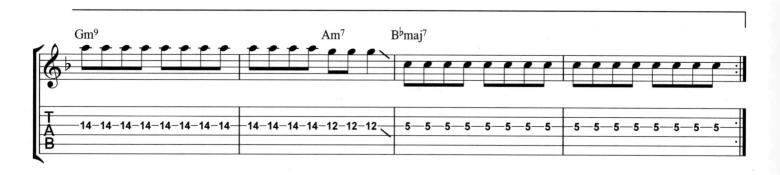

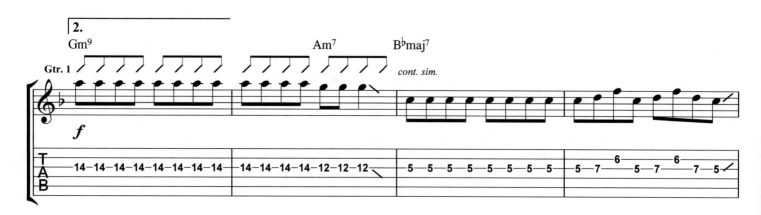

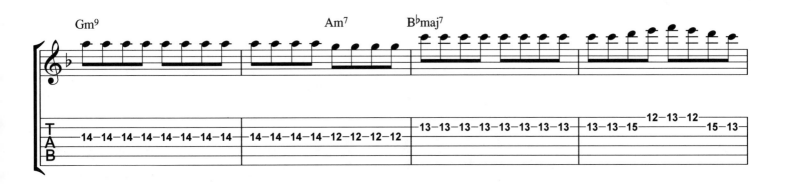

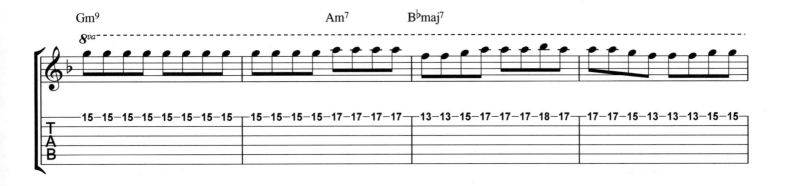

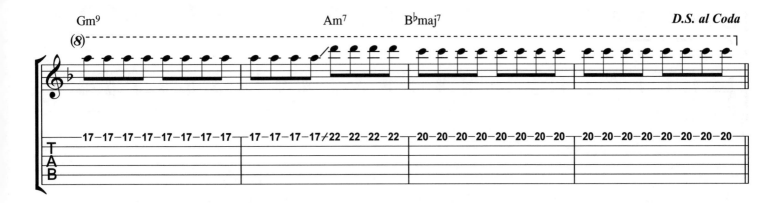

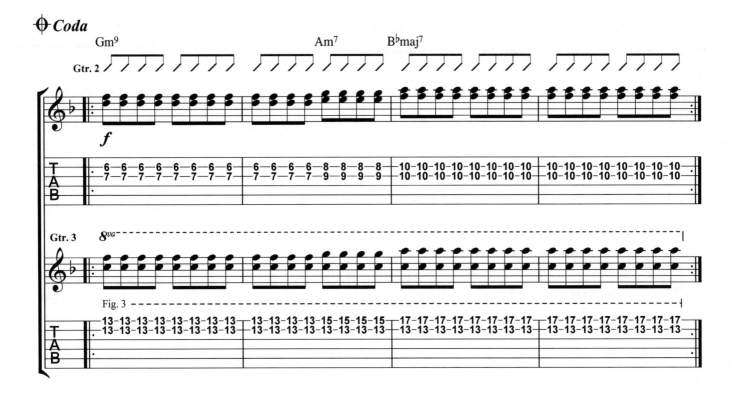

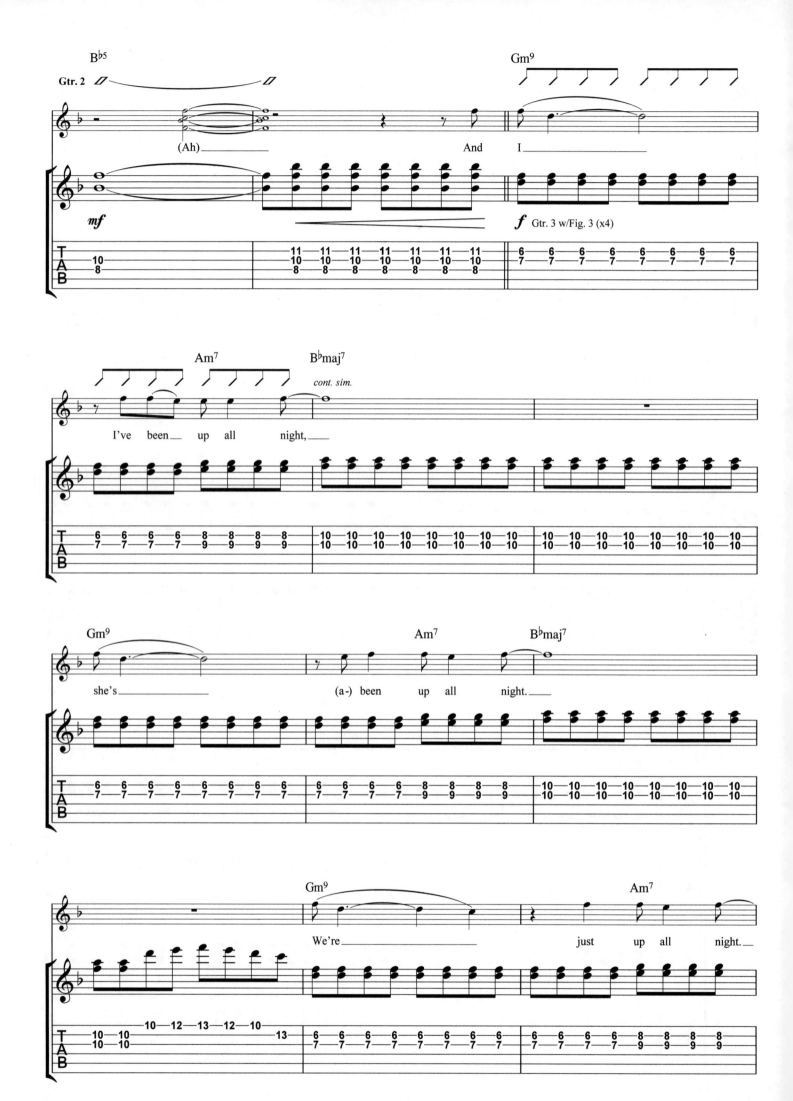

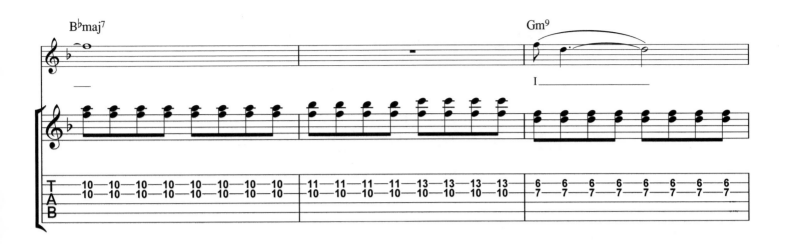

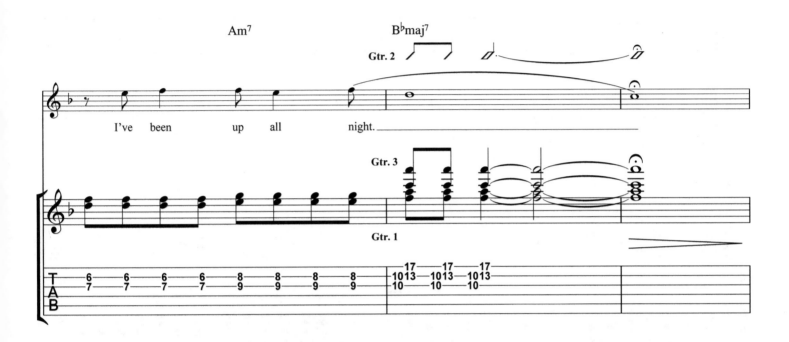

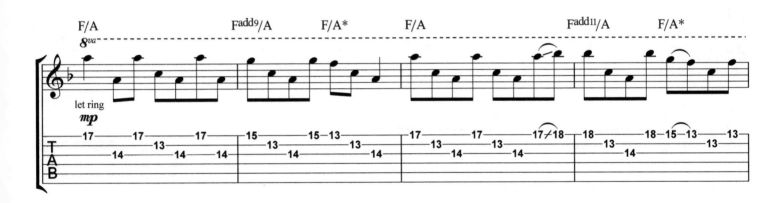

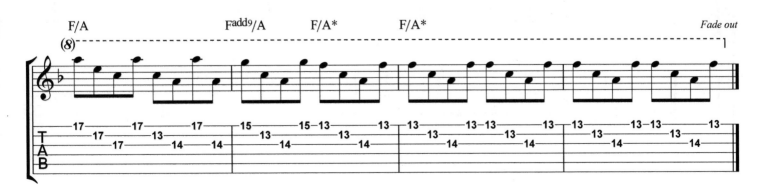

# Which Way Is Out

Song By Johnny Borrell
Music By Razorlight

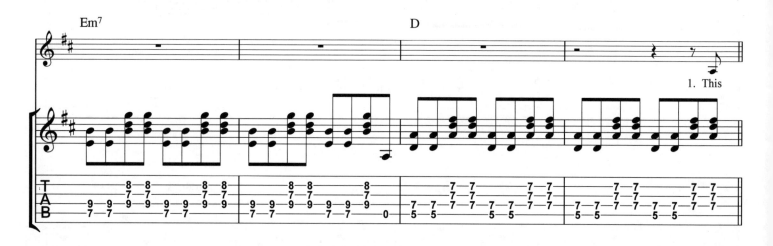

Verse

# Rip It Up

Song By Johnny Borrell
Music By Razorlight

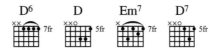

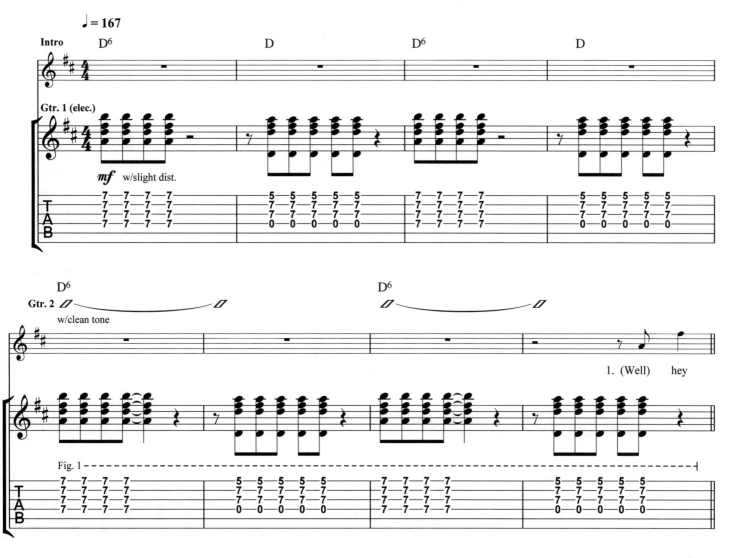

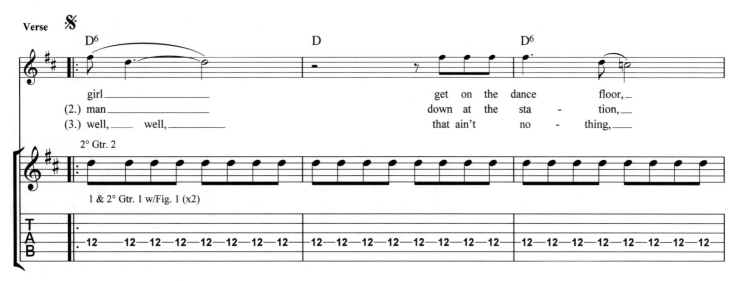

38

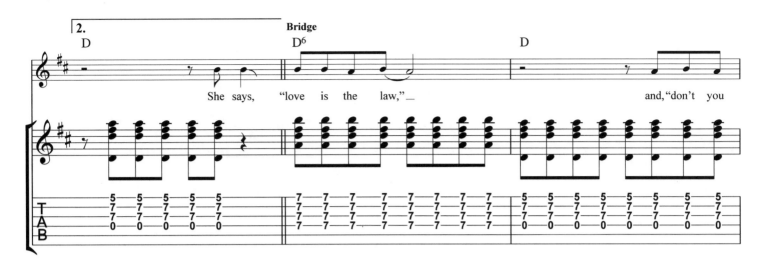

She says, "love is the law,"— and, "don't you

come round no more," she says, "I loved you so much more—

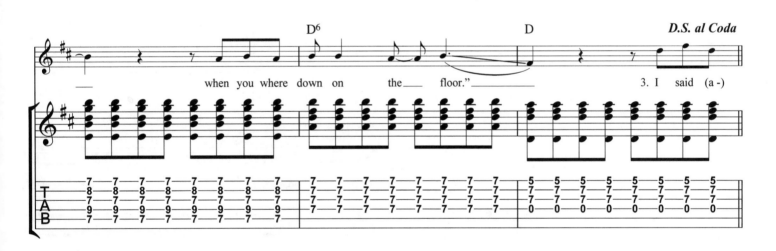

when you where down on the___ floor."___ 3. I said (a -)

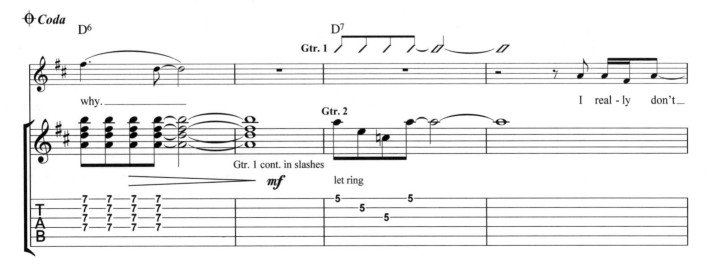

why.___ I real - ly don't___

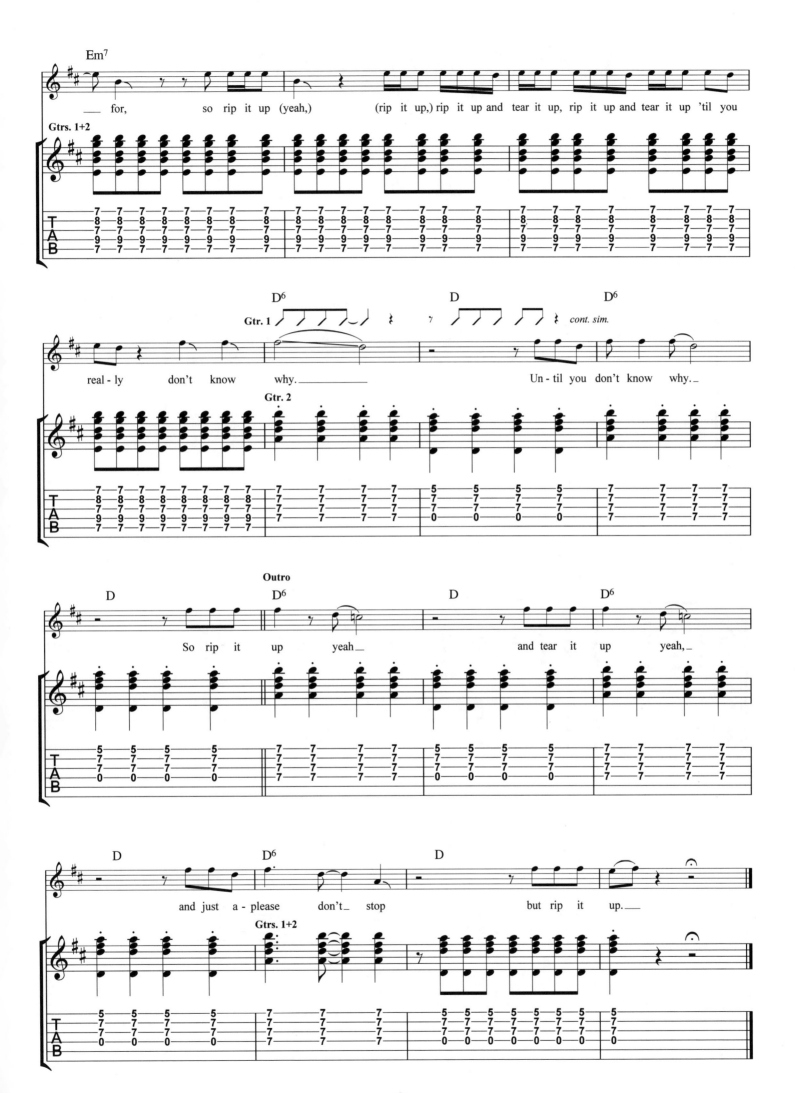

# Don't Go Back To Dalston

Song By Johnny Borrell
Music By Razorlight

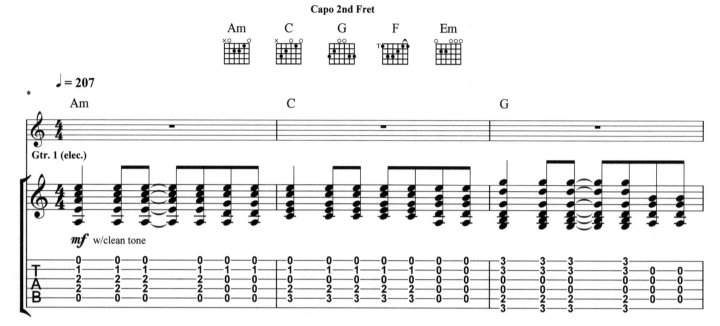

* Recorded key Bm - all Gtrs. capo 2nd fret

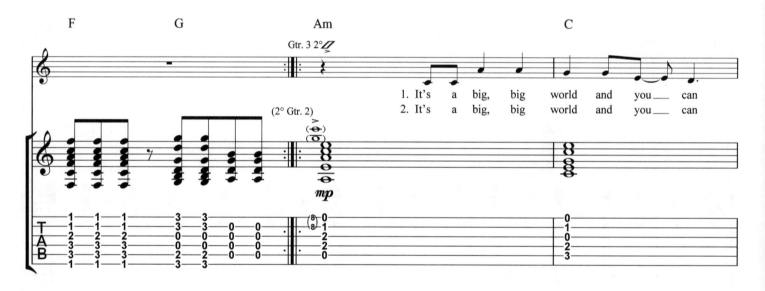

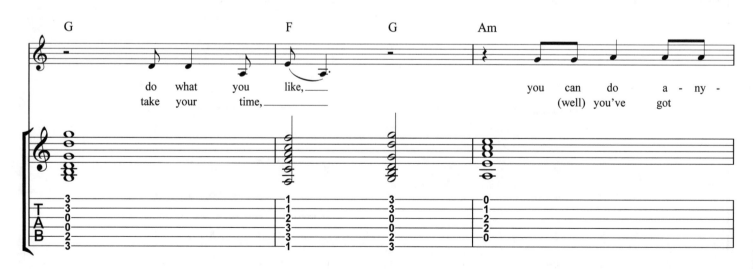

# Golden Touch

**Song By Johnny Borrell**
**Music By Razorlight**

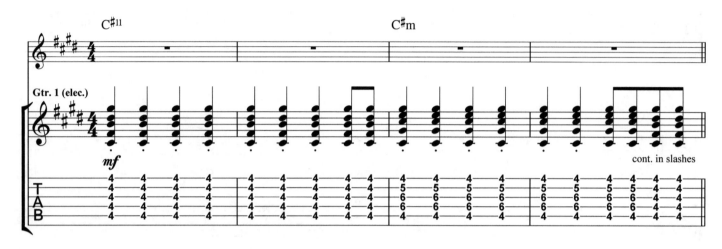

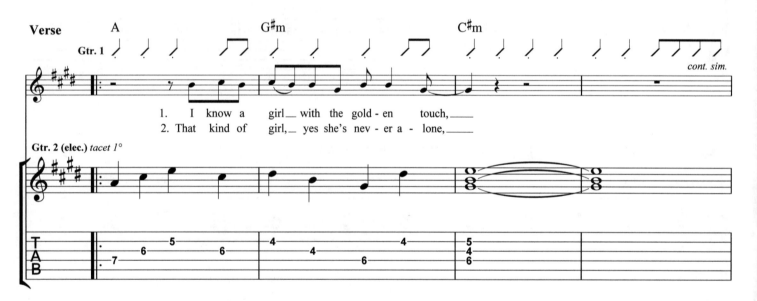

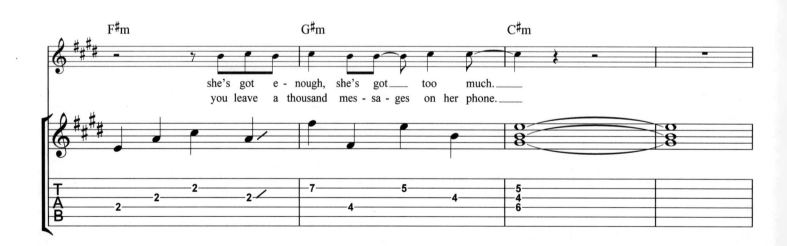

1. I know a girl with the gold-en touch,____
2. That kind of girl,____ yes she's nev-er a - lone,____

she's got e - nough, she's got____ too much.____
you leave a thousand mes-sa-ges on her phone.____

48

# Stumble And Fall

**Song By Johnny Borrell & Björn Ågren**
**Music By Razorlight**

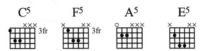

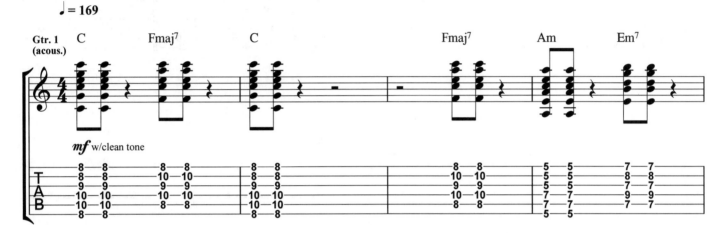

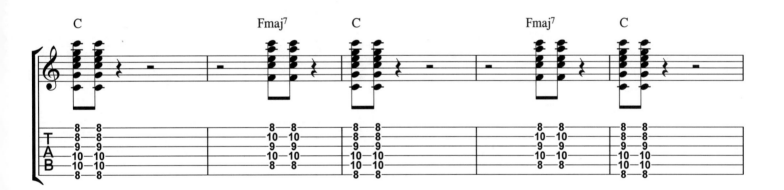

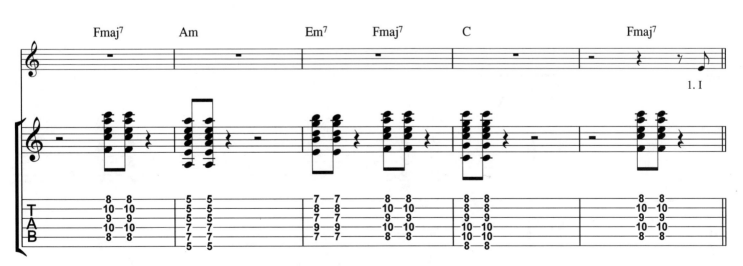

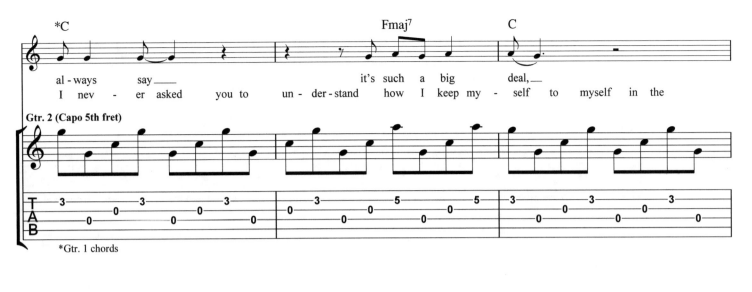

al - ways say\_\_\_\_ it's such a big deal,\_\_\_\_
I nev - er asked you to un - der - stand how I keep my - self to myself in the

Gtr. 2 (Capo 5th fret)

*Gtr. 1 chords

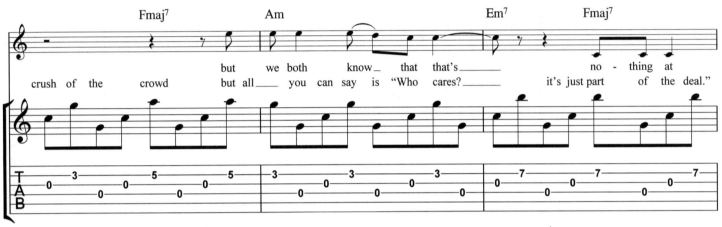

crush of the crowd but we both know\_\_ that that's_____ no - thing at
but all\_\_\_\_ you can say is "Who cares?_____ it's just part of the deal."

**Chorus**

all. And I'll get ov - er the br-

Gtr. 1 tacet

- eaks,_____ and I'll stum - ble and

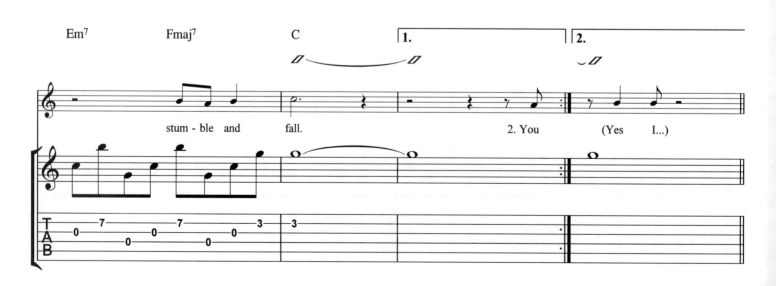

**Interlude**

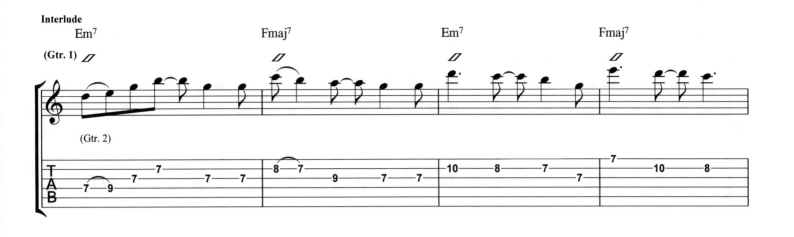

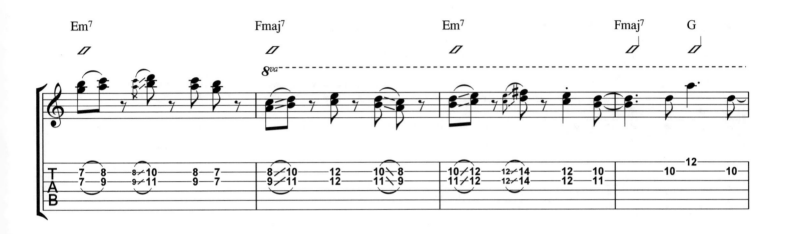

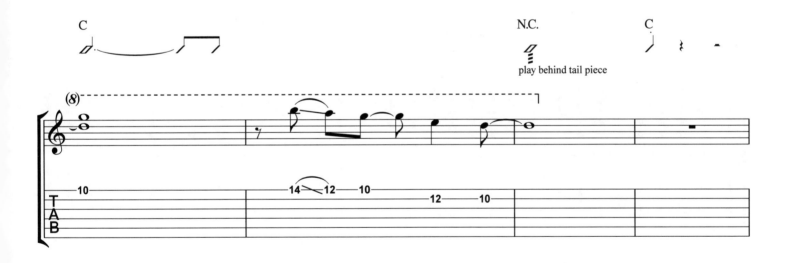

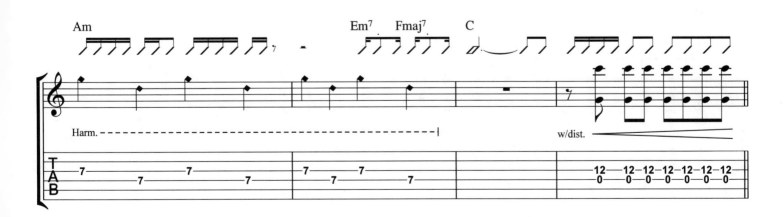

57

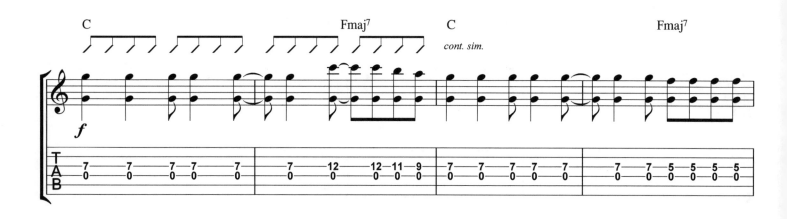

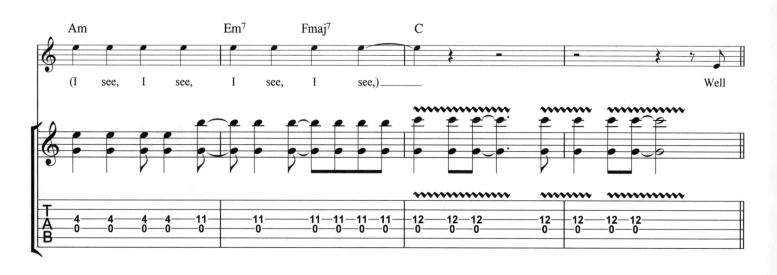

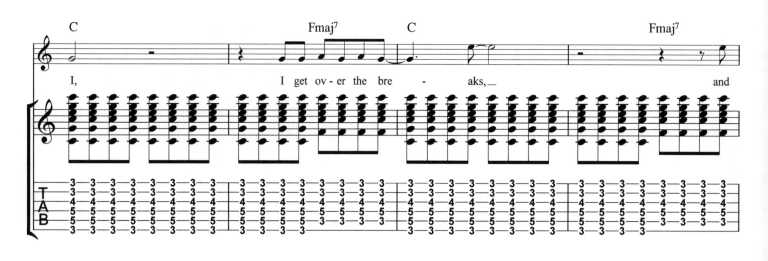

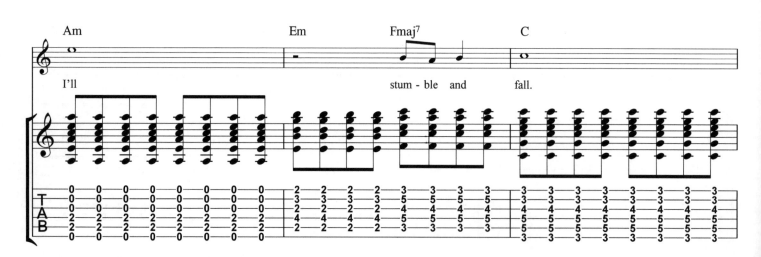

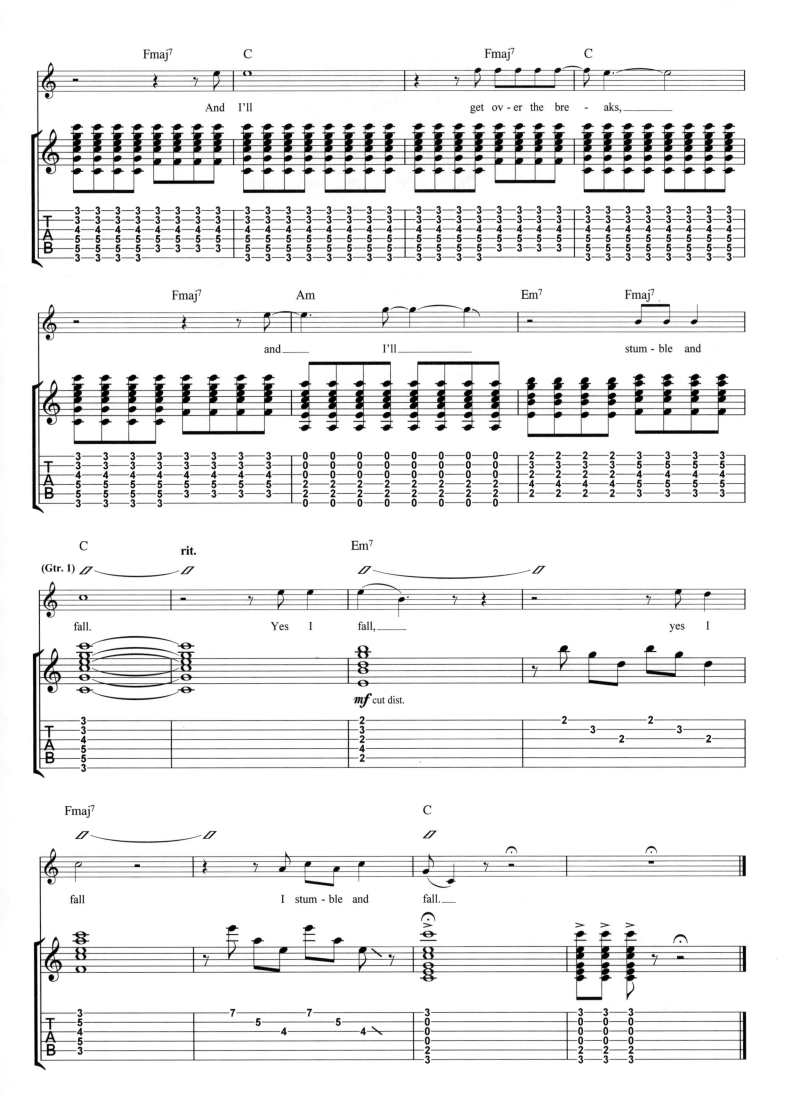

# Get It And Go

Song By Johnny Borrell
Music By Razorlight

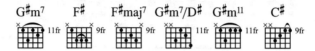

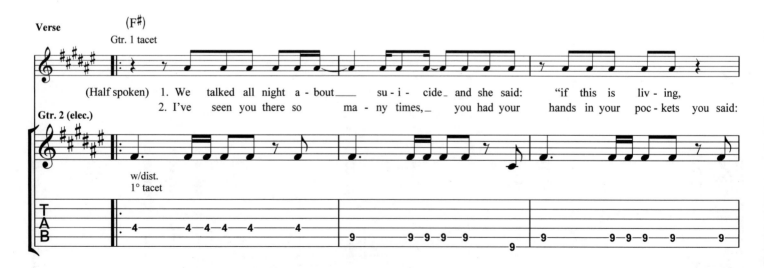

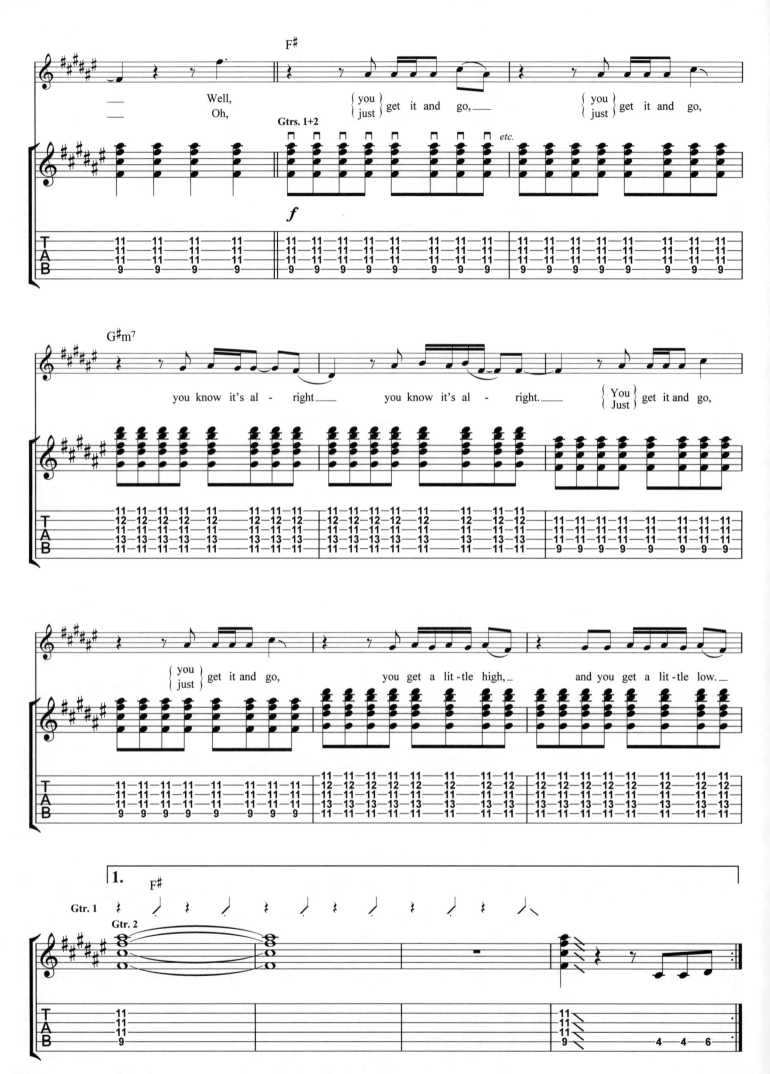

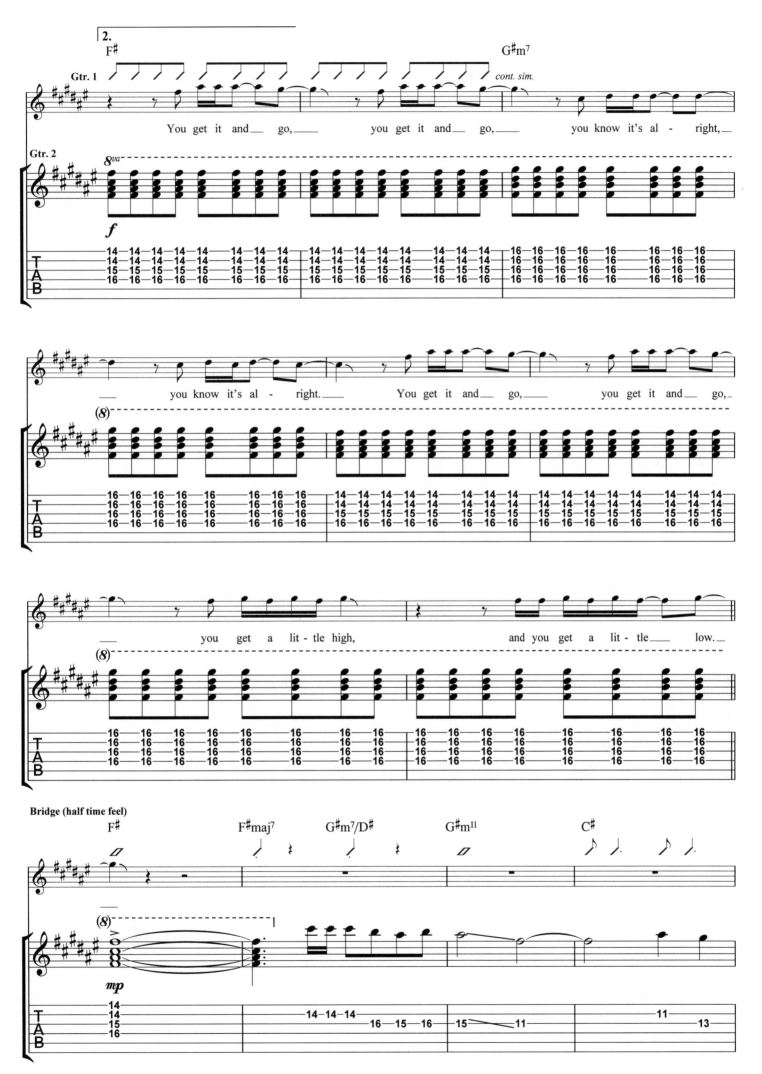

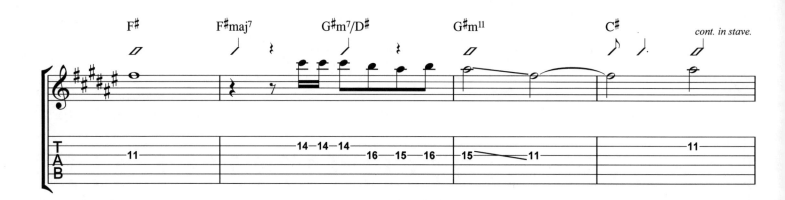

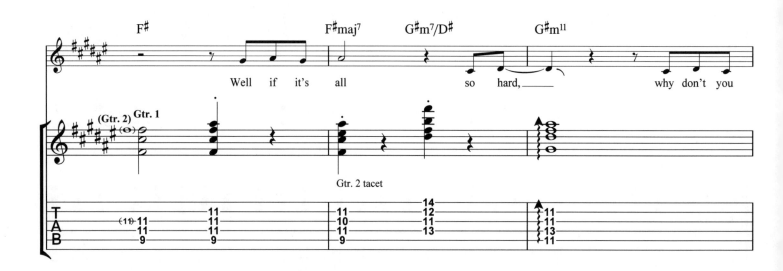

Well if it's all so hard,_____ why don't you

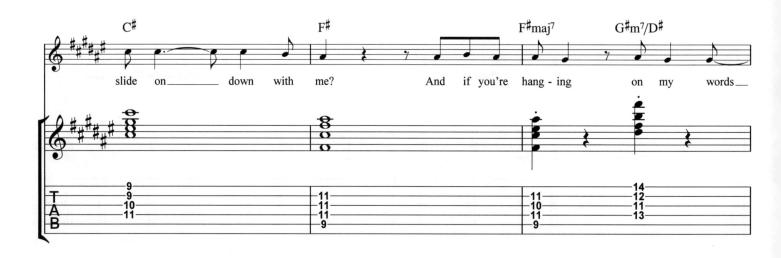

slide on_____ down with me? And if you're hang - ing on my words__

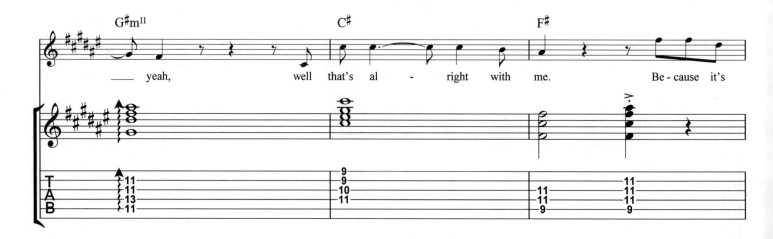

_____ yeah, well that's al - right with me. Be - cause it's

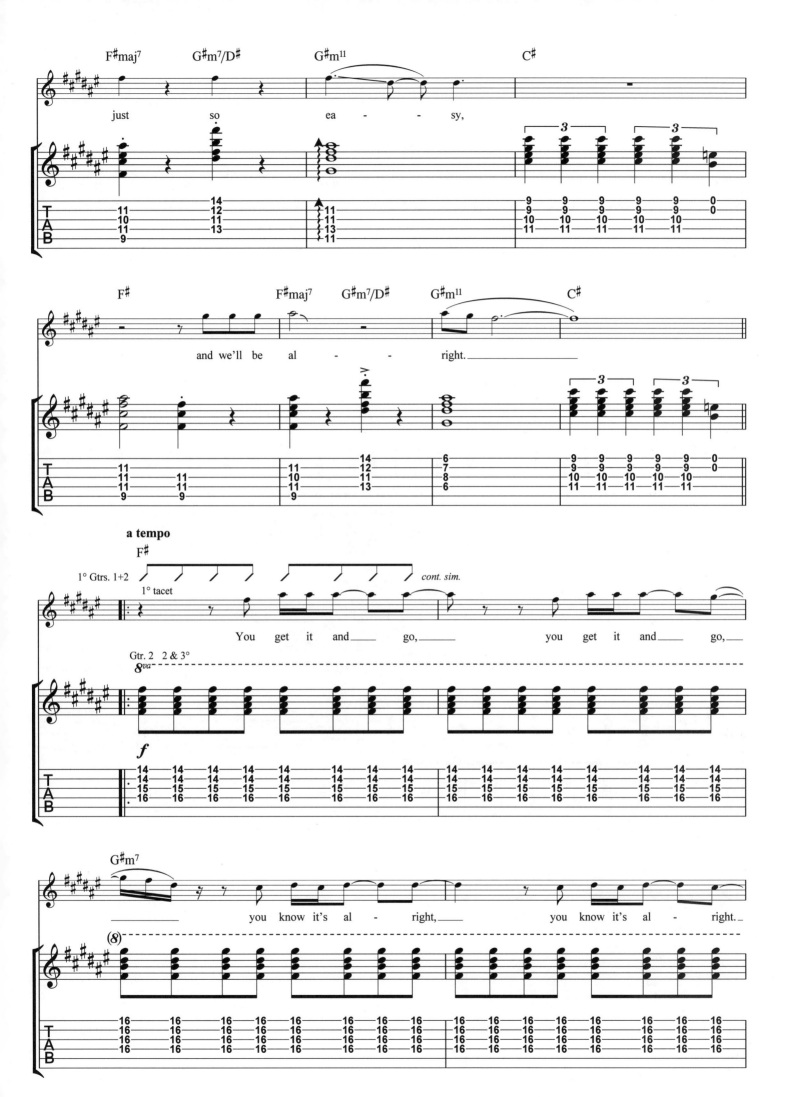

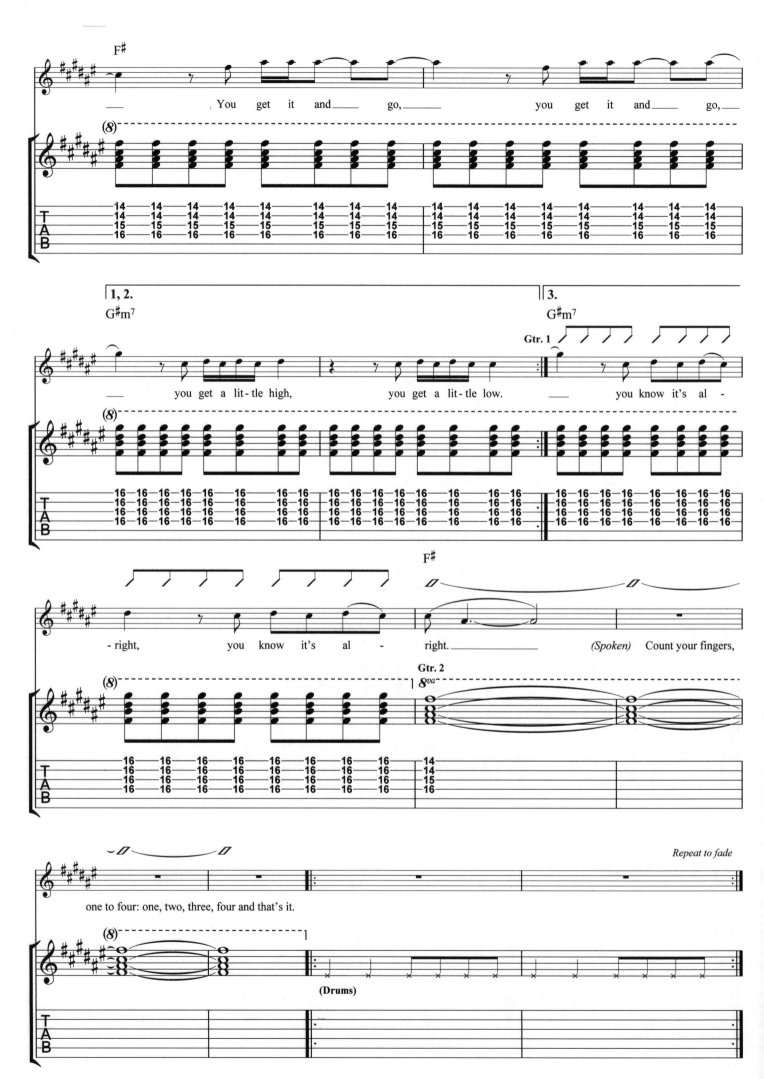

# In The City

Song By Johnny Borrell
Music By Razorlight

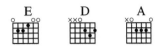

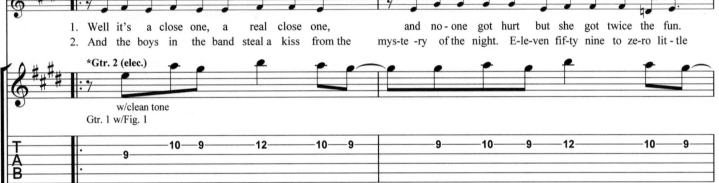

*2° part — 1° ad lib. si. (sparser)

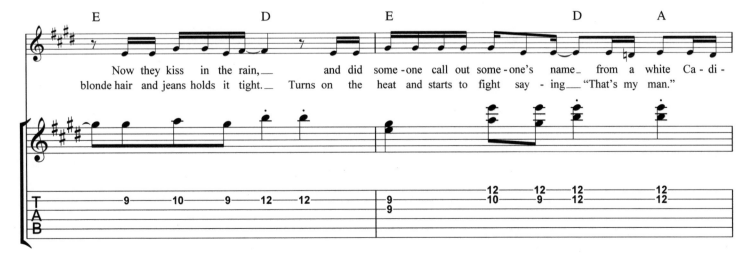

68

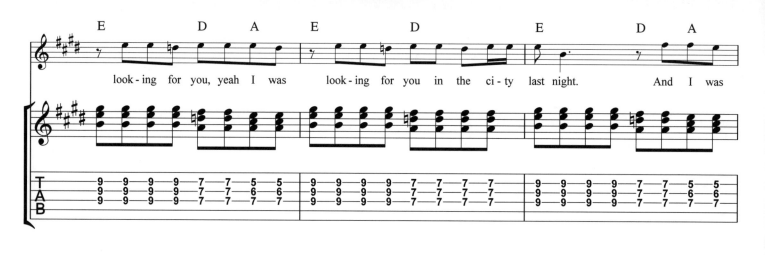

look-ing for you, yeah I was look-ing for you in the ci - ty last night. And I was

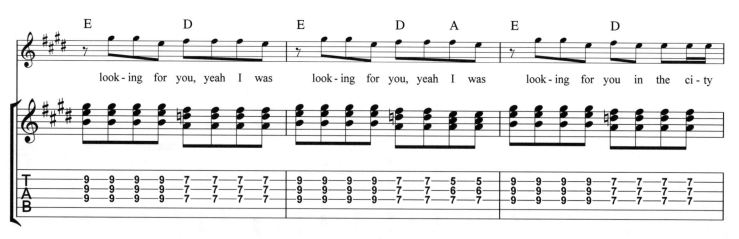

look-ing for you, yeah I was look-ing for you, yeah I was look-ing for you in the ci - ty

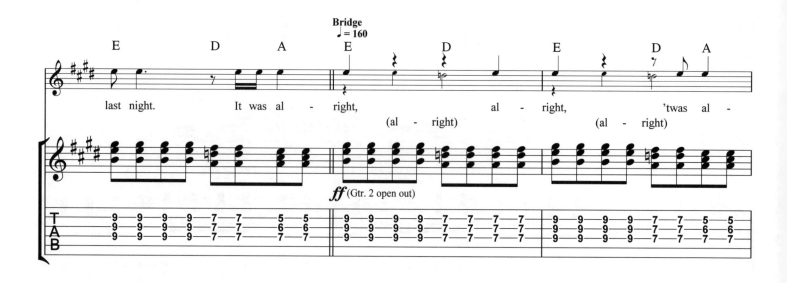

**Bridge**
♩ = 160

last night. It was al - right, al - right, 'twas al -
(al - right) (al - right)

*ff* (Gtr. 2 open out)

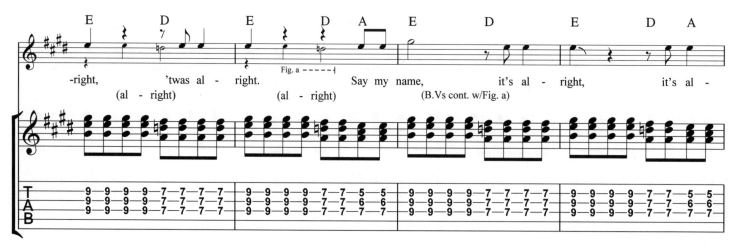

-right, 'twas al - right. Say my name, it's al - right, it's al -
(al - right) (al - right) (B.Vs cont. w/Fig. a)

Fig. a - - - - - ⌉

right, it's al - right just se - conds, just let go, just se - conds.

73

# To The Sea

## Song By Johnny Borrell & Björn Ågren
## Music By Razorlight

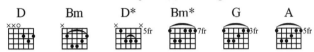

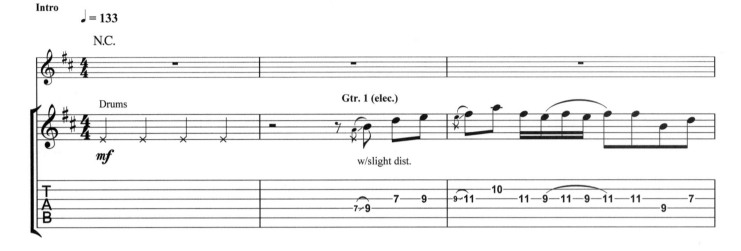

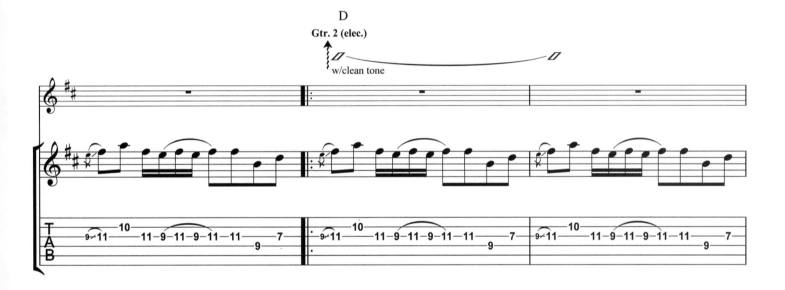

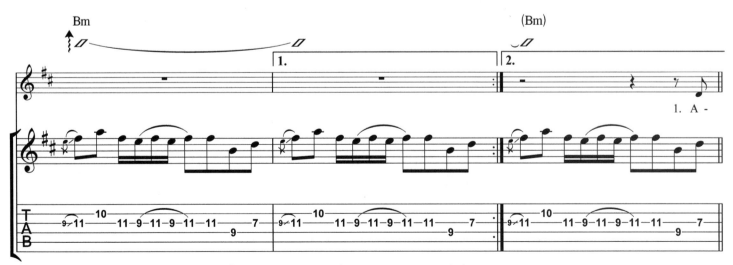

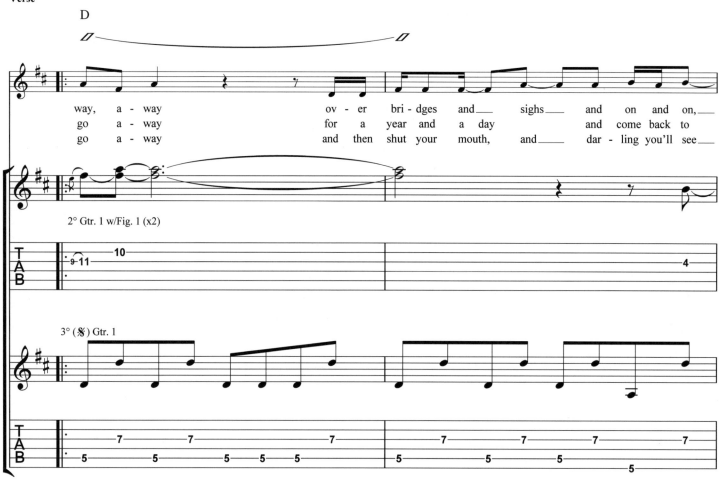

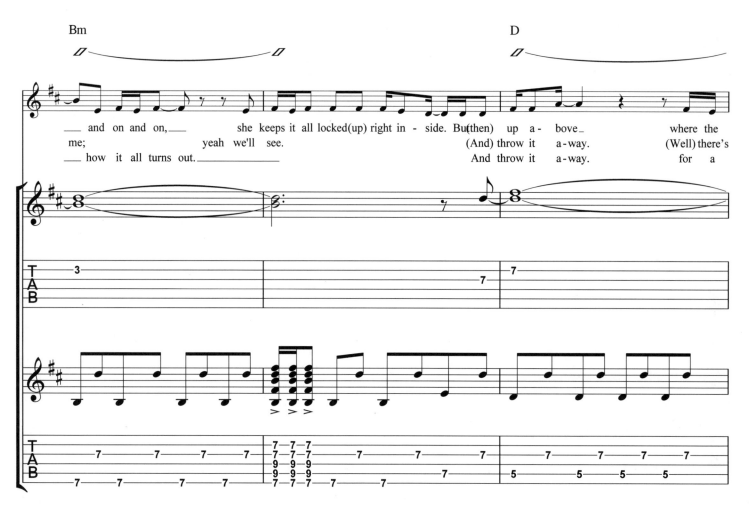

77

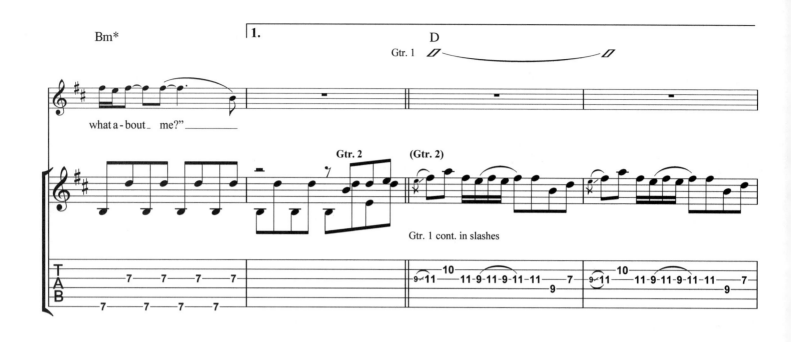

what a - bout _ me?" _____

Gtr. 1 cont. in slashes

2. (Yeah)

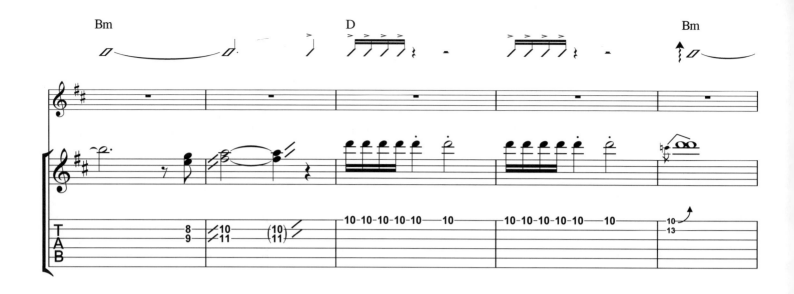

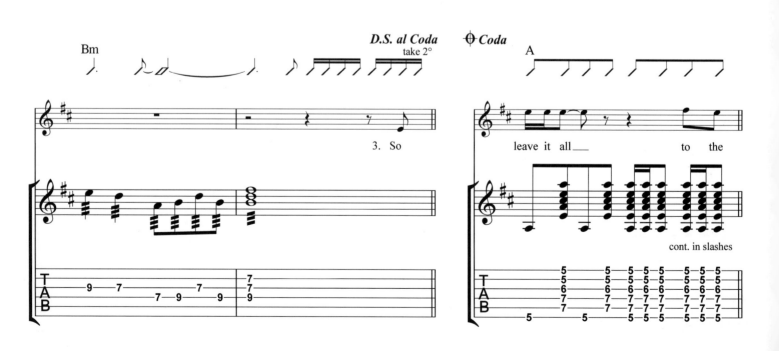

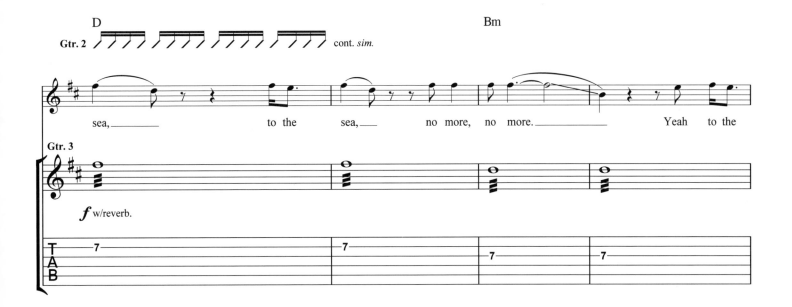

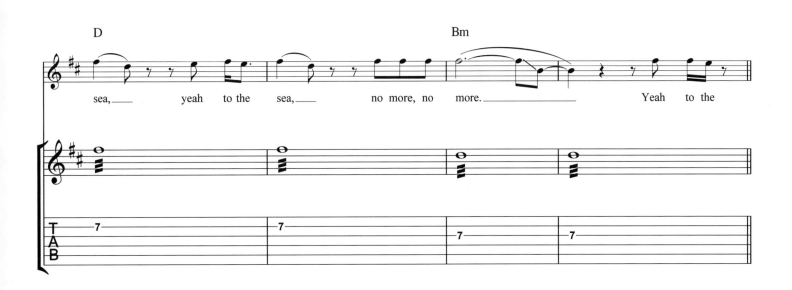

# Fall, Fall, Fall

Song By Johnny Borrell
Music By Razorlight

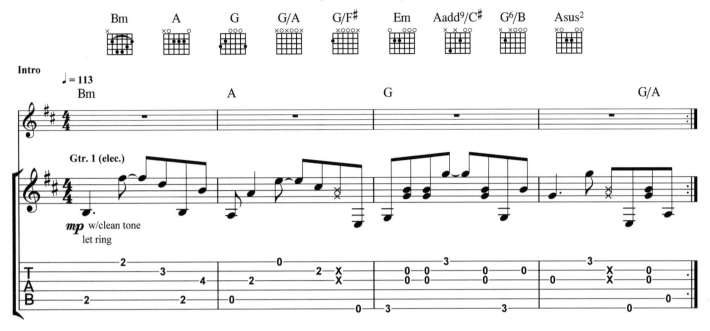

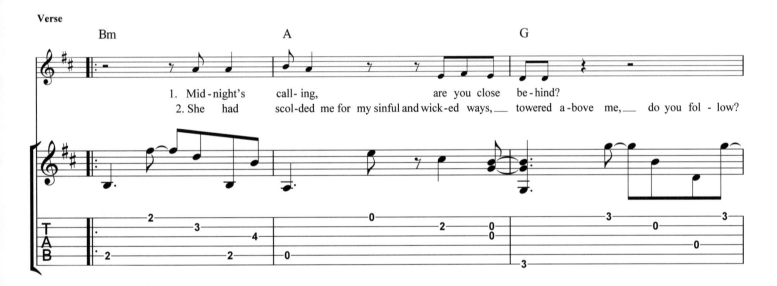

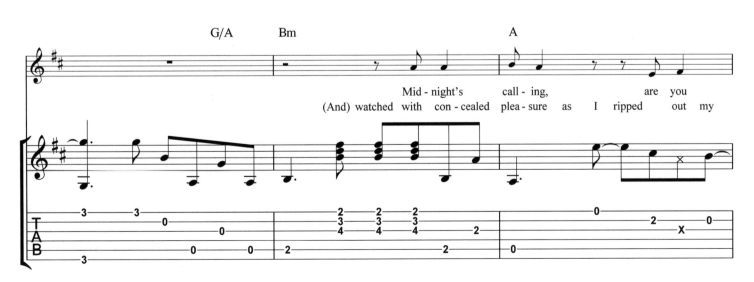

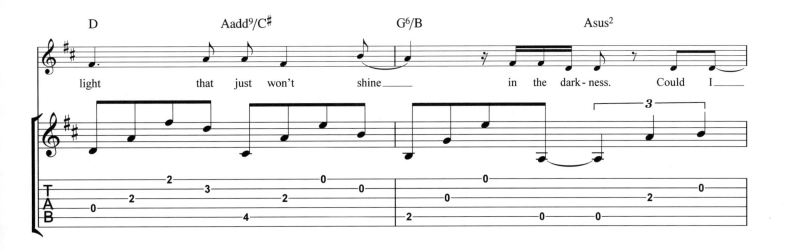

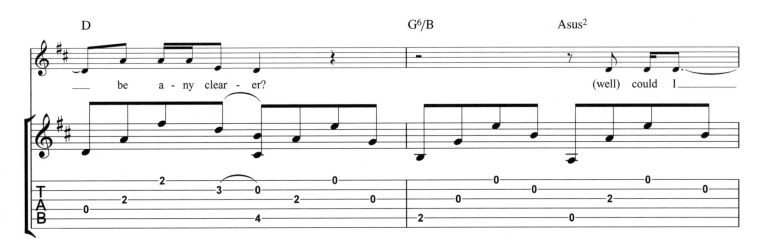

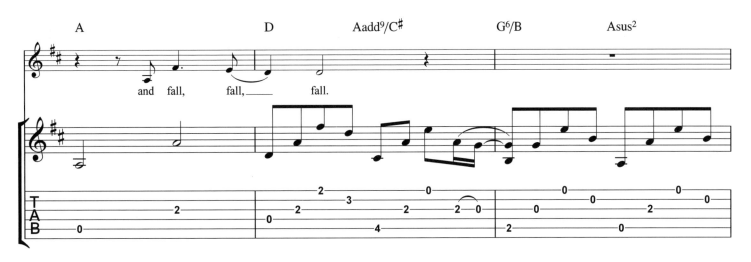

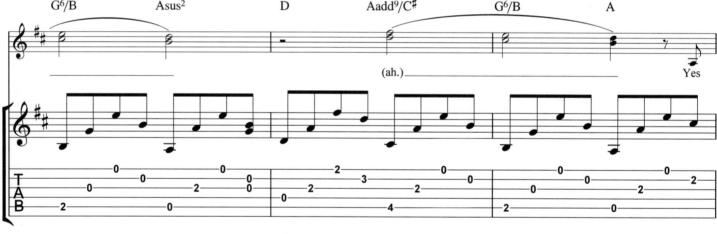

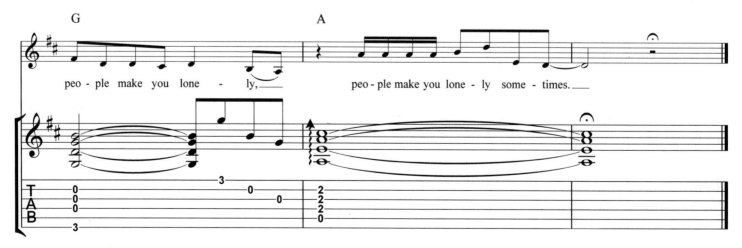

# Guitar Tablature Explained

**Guitar music can be notated in three different ways: on a musical stave, in tablature, and in rhythm slashes.**

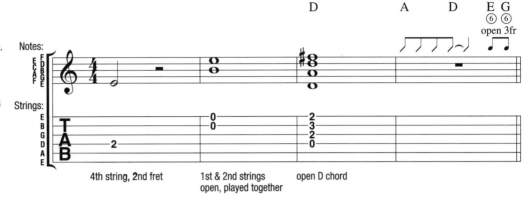

**RHYTHM SLASHES** are written above the stave. Strum chords in the rhythm indicated.?Round noteheads indicate single notes.

**THE MUSICAL STAVE** shows pitches and rhythms and is divided by lines into bars. Pitches are named after the first seven letters of the alphabet.

**TABLATURE** graphically represents the guitar fingerboard. Each horizontal line represents a string, and each number represents a fret.

4th string, 2nd fret    1st & 2nd strings open, played together    open D chord

## Definitions For Special Guitar Notation

**SEMI-TONE BEND:** Strike the note and bend up a semi-tone (1/2 step).

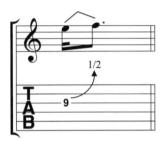

**WHOLE-TONE BEND:** Strike the note and bend up a whole-tone (whole step).

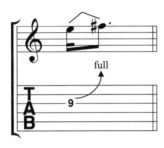

**GRACE NOTE BEND:** Strike the note and bend as indicated. Play the first note as quickly as possible.

**QUARTER-TONE BEND:** Strike the note and bend up a 1/4 step.

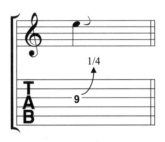

**BEND & RELEASE:** Strike the note and bend up as indicated, then release back to the original note.

**COMPOUND BEND & RELEASE:** Strike the note and bend up and down in the rhythm indicated.

**PRE-BEND:** Bend the note as indicated, then strike it.

**PRE-BEND & RELEASE:** Bend the note as indicated. Strike it and release the note back to the original pitch.

**UNISON BEND:** Strike the two notes simultaneously and bend the lower note up to the pitch of the higher.

**BEND & RESTRIKE:** Strike the note and bend as indicated then restrike the string where the symbol occurs.

**BEND, HOLD AND RELEASE:** Same as bend and release but hold the bend for the duration of the tie.

**BEND AND TAP:** Bend the note as indicated and tap the higher fret while still holding the bend.

**VIBRATO:** The string is vibrated by rapidly bending and releasing the note with the fretting hand.

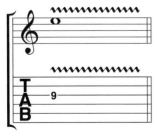

**HAMMER-ON:** Strike the first note with one finger, then sound the second note (on the same string) with another finger by fretting it without picking.

**PULL-OFF:** Place both fingers on the notes to be sounded, strike the first note and without picking, pull the finger off to sound the second note.

**LEGATO SLIDE (GLISS):** Strike the first note and then slide the same fret-hand finger up or down to the second note. The second note is not struck.

**NOTE:** The speed of any bend is indicated by the music notation and tempo.

**SHIFT SLIDE (GLISS & RESTRIKE):** Same as legato slide, except the second note is struck.

**TRILL:** Very rapidly alternate between the notes indicated by continuously hammering on and pulling off.

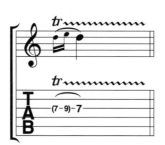

**TAPPING:** Hammer ("tap") the fret indicated with the pick-hand index or middle finger and pull off to the note fretted by the fret hand.

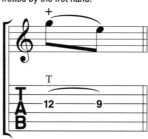

**PICK SCRAPE:** The edge of the pick is rubbed down (or up) the string, producing a scratchy sound.

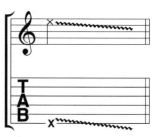

**MUFFLED STRINGS:** A percussive sound is produced by laying the fret hand across the string(s) without depressing, and striking them with the pick hand.

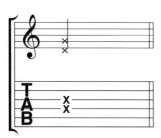

**NATURAL HARMONIC:** Strike the note while the fret-hand lightly touches the string directly over the fret indicated.

**PINCH HARMONIC:** The note is fretted normally and a harmonic is produced by adding the edge of the thumb or the tip of the index finger of the pick hand to the normal pick attack.

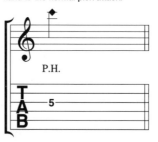

**HARP HARMONIC:** The note is fretted normally and a harmonic is produced by gently resting the pick hand's index finger directly above the indicated fret (in brackets) while plucking the appropriate string.

**PALM MUTING:** The note is partially muted by the pick hand lightly touching the string(s) just before the bridge.

**RAKE:** Drag the pick across the strings indicated with a single motion.

**TREMOLO PICKING:** The note is picked as rapidly and continuously as possible.

**ARPEGGIATE:** Play the notes of the chord indicated by quickly rolling them from bottom to top.

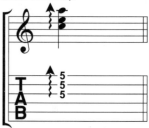

**SWEEP PICKING:** Rhythmic downstroke and/or upstroke motion across the strings.

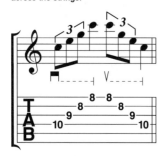

**VIBRATO DIVE BAR AND RETURN:** The pitch of the note or chord is dropped a specific number of steps (in rhythm) then returned to the original pitch.

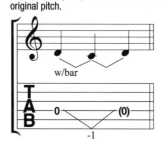

**VIBRATO BAR SCOOP:** Depress the bar just before striking the note, then quickly release the bar.

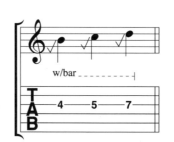

**VIBRATO BAR DIP:** Strike the note and then immediately drop a specific number of steps, then release back to the original pitch.

## additional musical definitions

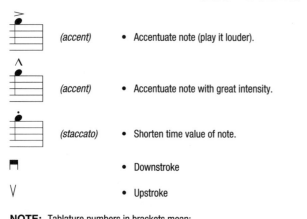

| | | |
|---|---|---|
| (accent) | • Accentuate note (play it louder). | |
| (accent) | • Accentuate note with great intensity. | |
| (staccato) | • Shorten time value of note. | |
| | • Downstroke | |
| | • Upstroke | |

**NOTE:** Tablature numbers in brackets mean:
1. The note is sustained, but a new articulation (such as hammer on or slide) begins.
2. A note may be fretted but not necessarily played.

*D.%. al Coda*

*D.C. al Fine*

tacet

• Go back to the sign (%), then play until the bar marked *To Coda* ⊕ then skip to the section marked ⊕ *Coda*.

• Go back to the beginning of the song and play until the bar marked *Fine*.

• Instrument is silent (drops out).

• Repeat bars between signs.

• When a repeated section has different endings, play the first ending only the first time and the second ending only the second time.

2 3 4 5 6 7 8 9
4/05 (54850)